Reading Comprehension

Book 2

Jo Browning Wroe
David Lambert

Acknowledgement

'What has happened to Lulu?' by Charles Causley is taken from *Figgie Hobbin* and reproduced by kind permission of Macmillan.

Reading Comprehension Book 2
LL05040
ISBN 1 85503 363 1
© Jo Browning Wroe and David Lambert
Illustrations by Mike Taylor, Felicity House and David Pattison
All rights reserved
First published 2003
Reprinted 2003 (June)

Printed in the UK for LDA
Duke Street, Wisbech, Cambs, PE13 2AE UK
3195 Wilson Drive NW, Grand Rapids, MI 49544 USA

Contents

Teacher's notes

Each book in the LDA Reading Comprehension series provides 33 stimulating photocopiable comprehension activities for the children you teach. In line with the National Literacy Strategy, the books present a wide variety of text types, including newspaper articles, poetry, dialogue, prose, instructions, charts and tables, letters, guidebook information and journal entries.

The activities are graded so that you will find a general trend of increasing conceptual complexity or discoursal organisation within the texts as you move through each section.

The four skill areas

To develop and hone your pupils' skills in four crucial areas of reading comprehension, the activities are grouped under the following headings:

Getting the main idea

In these activities, the pupils' overall grasp of the text is tested. To answer the questions, they are required to use their understanding of the text's main theme, argument or development.

Making inferences

The questions in this section encourage the pupils to make connections between the discrete elements embedded in the text. Pupils must choose, from a range of possibilities, the answer that is most *likely* to be true.

Noting details

Here, pupils are invited to scan the text for information and to retrieve discrete facts, for example an opening time, a date, or a figure. Occasionally, a more systematic reading is required to grasp the relationship between facts embedded in the text.

Using context clues

The questions in these activities encourage pupils to be sleuths, searching the textual environment for *clues* in order to select the most appropriate words or phrases to fill the blanks and complete the passage.

The questions

For each activity there are five questions that relate directly to the text. In most cases these are multiple choice and pupils simply have to circle the letters to indicate their answers. For the Noting details activities, pupils are required to write in their own answers.

At the end of each activity, there is a sixth, open-ended extension question. This is designed to encourage further reading, research, reflection or creativity on the same topic or a related one. These questions aim to personalise the text, making the issues raised within it relevant to the reader. There are three types of extension question:

Ask yourself

These questions tend to have an ethical slant and seek to develop pupils' critical thinking skills. For example, after an article about Diana, Princess of Wales:

Should famous people have more privacy? What are the arguments for and against?

Find out for yourself

These questions put the pupils in charge of their learning, inviting them to find out more about a subject. This might be done in a number of different ways, for example by using books, searching on the Web or asking people questions. It is usually left to the pupil to identify their own sources of reference, as each of these questions is very much a point of departure, not an end in itself. For example, following a page in a guide book about Roman roads in Italy:

There were many Roman roads built in Britain. Find out where some of them ran to and from and what they were called.

Express yourself

These questions encourage pupils to respond imaginatively and creatively to the texts they have read. They might be asked to write prose or poetry or to draw, design or make something. For example:

Find a book about origami and make your own origami model.

How do I use the book?

These Reading Comprehension books are intended to be a flexible teaching resource to use in the way that best enhances the learning going on in your classroom. The activities will fit well into the small group section of the literacy hour, but this is by no means the only appropriate context for the material. At the beginning of a school year, for example, they could be used as a tool to assess your pupils' level of comprehension and to find if there are particular areas of weakness which can then be addressed.

The texts should take no longer than 10 minutes to read and the questions no more than another 10 minutes to complete, although this will vary greatly from pupil to pupil.

In some circumstances, it may be beneficial for pupils to tackle the activities in pairs. In this way, less able pupils who lack confidence can provide each other with support as they read and then answer the questions.

There might also be occasions when it is helpful for a pupil to have access to the answers, in order to check their own work.

Answers

An answer key is provided at the back of the book on page 64.

William Shakespeare

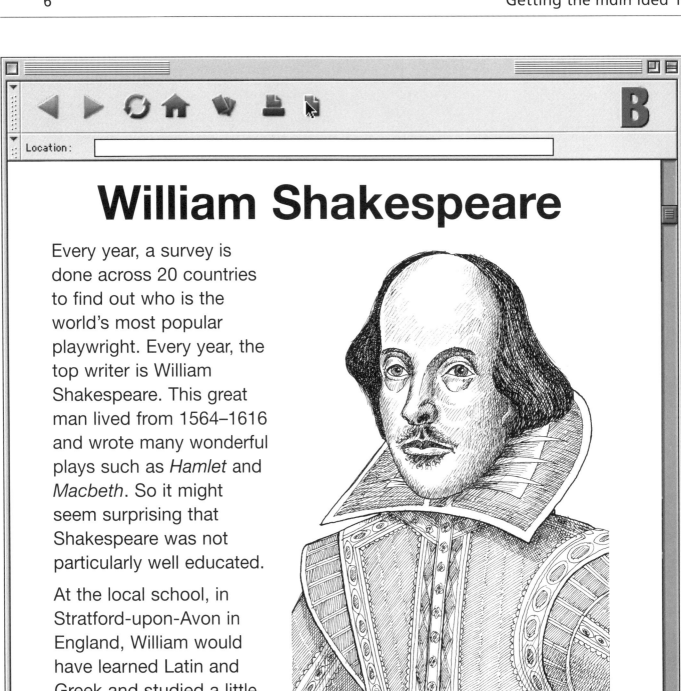

Every year, a survey is done across 20 countries to find out who is the world's most popular playwright. Every year, the top writer is William Shakespeare. This great man lived from 1564–1616 and wrote many wonderful plays such as *Hamlet* and *Macbeth*. So it might seem surprising that Shakespeare was not particularly well educated.

At the local school, in Stratford-upon-Avon in England, William would have learned Latin and Greek and studied a little history. However, he left school at the age of 11, so the experts don't really understand how he went on to write such brilliant plays. Where did he get his ideas? Some people think that Shakespeare did not write the plays at all. They think that the secret author was an aristocrat, such as a duke or a lord, who would have had a good education. Perhaps the real author did not want anyone to know his name. Others say that several people must have written the 32 plays and over 100 poems! We may never know the truth, but whoever wrote them, Shakespeare is still the tops.

Freddie Godfrey 2013
Connor Connor

William Shakespeare

Read the text carefully and circle the best ending for each sentence.

 Shakespeare was born in the
a) 1500s.
b) 1600s.
c) 1700s.

 The survey tries to discover
a) who writes the world's favourite plays.
b) why Shakespeare is so popular.
c) who likes Shakespeare.

 Hamlet and *Macbeth* are
a) novels.
b) poems.
c) plays.

 Some experts believe Shakespeare's plays were written by
a) a Greek.
b) a more educated person.
c) a more popular writer.

 An aristocrat is
a) a secret author.
b) someone who writes plays.
c) a duke or a lord.

Find out for yourself
Macbeth is one of Shakespeare's most well-known works. What is the story in this tragedy?

Wolf Children

You probably know Mowgli in the cartoon film *The Jungle Book*. Mowgli was based on the true story of an Indian boy raised by wolves.

There are several astonishing stories of wild wolves raising human babies with their own cubs as part of the wolf family. It has happened when abandoned children have been rescued by wolves and suckled with the milk of their wolf mothers. There have been cases in the forests of India, the far-eastern parts of Russia and the plains of central Europe.

The children live as wolves, howling, walking on all fours and hunting with the pack. Naturally they fear man, and the wolf children that have been caught put up a fierce fight, biting and snarling just like wolves. As you can imagine, these wolf children are filthy, with matted hair and long finger and toe nails.

Experts who study these rare children find it hard to discover exactly what happened. The wolf children, of course, do not have human language to tell them.

Wolf Children

Read the text carefully and circle the best ending for each sentence.

1. 'Wolf children' are
   a) boys or girls left by their parents.
   b) boys like Mowgli.
   c) just stories and don't really exist.

2. 'Suckled' means
   a) eaten.
   b) rescued.
   c) fed.

3. Stories of wolf children have come from
   a) all over the world.
   b) mainly India.
   c) India, Russia and Europe.

4. Human children raised by wolves
   a) never adapt to the pack.
   b) behave just like wolves.
   c) want to find human parents.

5. Studying wolf children is difficult because they
   a) cannot talk in human language.
   b) walk on four legs.
   c) smell awful.

Ask yourself

Cases of wolf children are extremely rare. Is it right to 'rescue' wolf children or should they be left with the pack? Give reasons for your answer.

Working Dogs

Dogs were the first animal to be domesticated, that is to live with people. In the past, people used dogs' natural instinct to defend the pack. Dogs were kept to protect the 'human pack' and used in battle.

Nowadays, dogs are used in all sorts of ways. There are some jobs that even today's advanced technology cannot do as well as a dog. Their highly developed sense of smell makes 'sniffer dogs' excellent at detecting drugs and explosives smuggled by passengers or in luggage at ports and airports. This sense of smell, together with their acute hearing, also makes dogs valuable workers in finding victims trapped under collapsed buildings after earthquakes.

You've probably seen guide dogs or 'seeing-eye' dogs, helping blind people across busy streets. Not all breeds of dog would be suited to such responsible work. Calm, reliable Labradors and Alsatians (German shepherds) do it best. An excitable red setter would be no good at all!

Sometimes dogs do not even have to work hard to be useful. Scientists have discovered that elderly people who live on their own have longer and healthier lives if they have the companionship of 'man's best friend'.

DOGS

Working Dogs

Read the text carefully and circle the best ending for each sentence.

 1 Dogs will defend humans because
a) their instinct is to defend the pack.
b) they like humans.
c) they like fighting.

2 'Sniffer dogs' are dogs who
a) like travelling.
b) are used to find drugs and explosives.
c) like working with technology.

3 After an earthquake, dogs can help by
a) smelling buried victims.
b) seeing and hearing buried victims.
c) smelling and hearing buried victims.

4 The best sort of dog for a blind person would be
a) a calm, reliable dog.
b) an excitable dog.
c) any large breed of dog.

5 Scientists have found that dogs are especially good for
a) old people's homes.
b) elderly people who are still working.
c) elderly people living by themselves.

Find out for yourself
Many of the different breeds of dog were originally bred to do particular kinds of work. Find out about some working breeds and what jobs they do.

Diana, Princess of Wales

In 1981, aged just 20, a young girl called Diana Spencer married Prince Charles and instantly became Diana, Princess of Wales.

Everyone thought that one day she would become the Queen of England. Sadly, the fun-loving Diana felt trapped in the marriage. The British royal family expected her to behave in certain ways and she felt that she did not fit in. Diana became depressed and angry. Finally, in 1992 she and Prince Charles divorced. They had two sons, Princes William and Harry, who continued to see both of their parents.

At the end of the long hot summer of 1997, Diana at last found happiness with a new partner, Dodi Al Fayed. It was then that tragedy struck. One night, as they were being driven through the streets of Paris, newspaper photographers spotted the famous couple and chased them. The driver accelerated into an underground tunnel. He lost control of the car and it crashed inside the tunnel. Dodi and the driver were killed immediately. Diana and her bodyguard were rushed to the nearest hospital.

The announcement came on the morning of 31 August 1997: 'Princess Diana is dead'. Everyone who heard the shocking news remembers where they were and exactly what they were doing at that moment.

Diana, Princess of Wales

Read the text carefully and circle the best ending for each sentence.

 Diana Spencer became Princess of Wales because
a) she came from Wales.
b) she married Prince Charles.
c) she was just 20.

 The couple divorced because
a) they were unhappy together.
b) Diana did not want to be queen.
c) Diana found happiness with Dodi.

 Dodi Al Fayed was Diana's
a) photographer.
b) driver.
c) boyfriend.

 The driver of the car drove faster to
a) escape the photographers.
b) get out of the tunnel.
c) get to the hospital.

 People remember what they were doing when they heard the announcement because
a) it was a long hot summer.
b) the news was so shocking.
c) it was early in the morning.

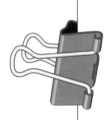

Ask yourself
Should famous people have more privacy? What are the arguments for and against?

Bettacare Mail Order Catalogue

1 Fish Shower Radio

REF: 2634

No more singing in the shower! You can listen to your favourite radio station instead! This fully-waterproof AM/FM radio looks just like a tropical fish and sticks to tiles with suction caps.

Colours:
aqua, jade or yellow

Requires 2 AA batteries (not included)   **£14.99**

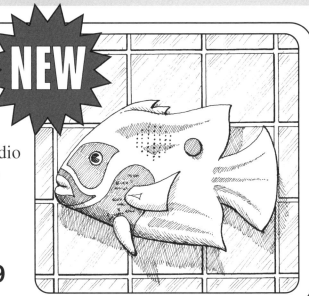

NEW

2 Bug Trappa

REF: 8437

You'll never have to go near another creepy crawly! Simply place the head of the Bug Trappa over the insect, twist the pole and watch as the shutter closes – and traps your prey! Then, simply release the bug outside by twisting the pole.

Length: 40 cms   **£ 8.99**

NEW ROTATING HEAD ACTION

3 Chirpy-chirpy Water Me!

REF: 2746

Take the guesswork out of watering your pot plants! This attractive water gauge has water-sensitive probes that measure moisture levels in the soil around the roots of your plants. When the little bird chirps, they need water! It's light sensitive too, so it won't wake you up at night.

Colours: red robin, petrol-green hummingbird or yellow budgie

Requires cell batteries (not included)   **£12.99**

Bettacare Mail Order Catalogue

Read the text carefully and circle the best ending for each sentence.

 The Fish Shower Radio allows you to
a) sing in the shower.
b) play radio programmes to your tropical fish.
c) listen to a radio programme in the shower.

2 The Bug Trappa lets you
a) kill insects that get into the house.
b) catch insects in the house and then take them outside.
c) catch insects outside and bring them into the house.

3 The Chirpy-chirpy Water Me chirps
a) when the plant roots are wet.
b) when the plant roots are dry.
c) at night.

4 'Light sensitive' here means
a) it does not work in the dark.
b) it only works in the dark.
c) it is light and easy to carry.

5 This mail order catalogue sells
a) toys for children.
b) equipment for wildlife enthusiasts.
c) devices to help around the house.

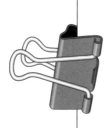

Express yourself

Invent a device to help you round the house or at school. (Think of a job you don't like doing!) Then design the advertisement for it.

Spinning

If you have looked at a bit of matted sheep's wool caught on a fence, you will realise that it could not be used straight from the sheep for knitting a jumper or weaving cloth. First it has to be spun into yarn. Ever since the 18th century, this has been done by machines in factories, but before then, spinning was done by people at home.

Before the wool could be spun, it had to be cleaned and then carded. For carding, you would need two wide combs with rows of steel teeth. You would put a piece of wool on one comb and then pull the other comb across the wool again and again. When you had finished, the wool fibres would be straight and smooth, ready for spinning.

Spinning is simply twisting the fibres into a single strand and stretching it out into a long, even length. It is a long process but a spinning wheel helps the pulling and twisting. The spinner holds the wool in one hand and twists one end onto the yarn already in the spindle. The spinning wheel turns the spindle and pulls the wool into yarn, winding it onto the spindle at the same time.

In some places, people still make their own yarn like this because they want to keep the art of spinning alive.

Spinning

Read the text carefully and circle the best ending for each sentence.

 Wool has to be spun before it can
   a) be used for weaving or knitting.
   b) be taken from the sheep.
   c) be taken to a factory.

 Carding is a process that
   a) you use to make cardigans.
   b) gets the wool ready for spinning.
   c) cleans the wool.

 Spinning wheels
   a) were used from the 18th century onwards.
   b) made spinning easier for people working in factories.
   c) made spinning easier for people at home.

 Spinning
   a) turns wool into yarn.
   b) turns yarn into wool.
   c) turns wool into spindles.

 Nowadays spinning wheels
   a) are banned because people might prick their fingers.
   b) are used by a few people.
   c) are used in factories all over the world.

Ask yourself

Do you think there is any point in keeping old-fashioned skills alive, if machines can do the job better?
Give reasons for your answer.

Super Soups

Good soups are really only about good ingredients. Some soups can be prepared, cooked and on the table in minutes – and still be as tasty as one that you have spent an hour or so preparing.

Anyone can make soup. It can be as simple as sweating some fragrant vegetables over a low heat, adding a little stock, and that's it. You can also throw in some herbs or spices for extra flavour if you like. Then you just have to choose whether you want your soup chunky or puréed like baby food. (After all, we all like baby food, don't we?) To make it a bit special, you can serve it with cream or some croutons on the top.

You can make soups out of just about anything, and with a little bit of imagination they can be delicious. Whenever I make a soup, I always make enough for 4 or 6, even if it is only for me. Then I freeze the extra in those little sandwich bags. (Freezing doesn't do the soup any favours but it will *still* be nicer than anything you can buy in a shop!)

The following recipes are all easy and take no more than half an hour from the moment you reach for the chopping board…

Super Soups

Read the text carefully and circle the best ending for each sentence.

 1 A good soup
a) takes an hour or so to prepare.
b) doesn't have to take a long time to make.
c) is never finished.

 2 The main ingredients for soup are usually
a) vegetables and stock.
b) vegetables and herbs.
c) stock and baby food.

 3 Soup can be served with cream for
a) breakfast.
b) a baby.
c) a special occasion.

 4 The writer always makes enough soup for at least 4 people, so he
a) can invite friends for dinner.
b) freeze some for another day.
c) have second helpings.

 5 When fresh soup has been frozen, it
a) doesn't taste quite as good as when it was fresh.
b) tastes better than when it was fresh.
c) tastes worse than soup you buy in a shop.

Find out for yourself
Find two recipes for soup that use completely different ingredients.

Enter our brand new competition and win one of our fabulous prizes!

It's easy! Just tell us why Brekkypops is your favourite breakfast cereal and you could be one of our top prize-winners.

So hurry, because we're giving away hundreds of prizes worth over £200,000!

- 20 widescreen TVs • 20 DVD players • 20 camcorders • 50 computer games
- 50 digital cameras • 50 snooker tables • 50 mini-disc players • 50 table football games
- 100 vouchers for leading sportswear outlets • 100 vouchers for Bestburger fast-food outlets
- 100 vouchers for Splashing Towers amusement parks

Simply collect the entry tokens from 5 packets of Regular, Forest Fruit 'n' Nut or new Tropical Fruit Flavoured Brekkypops and stick them to this entry form.

-------Cut along dotted line ✂---

I just love eating Brekkypops because _____

_____

_____(No more than 30 words)

Send your entry to: Brekkypops Promotion, Box 2000, Basingstoke BS49 2RE

Terms and conditions

1. This offer is open to all UK residents with the exception of employees of International Cereals Inc., their families and all persons professionally connected with this promotion. 2. Parental consent is required before winners under the age of 18 can collect their prizes. 3. Offer closes 20 September 2004.

Brekkypops

Read the text carefully and circle the best ending for each sentence.

⟨1⟩ Brekkypops is probably a cereal made for
   a) elderly people.
   b) babies and toddlers.
   c) children and teenagers.

⟨2⟩ The prizes include
   a) electronic games and fast-food vouchers.
   b) electronic games and holidays.
   c) computers and sportswear vouchers.

⟨3⟩ Your entry should say
   a) why you want to win.
   b) what you most like for breakfast.
   c) why you like Brekkypops.

⟨4⟩ To win a prize you have to
   a) live in Basingstoke.
   b) be over 18.
   c) have a parent's agreement if you are below 18.

⟨5⟩ If a member of your family works for the company that makes
   Brekkypops,
   a) you have a better chance of winning.
   b) you can't win a prize unless your family agrees.
   c) you can't enter the competition.

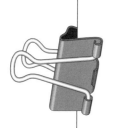

Express yourself

Design a breakfast cereal competition. What is
the name of your cereal? What will competitors
have to do? What prizes will you offer?

Gardening Through the Seasons

Of all the seasons, spring remains the greatest miracle. Even in the tiniest patch of garden, it never ceases to amaze when the first bright green shoots appear. It can still be chilly, but the days are starting to get longer and the cheery yellows of spring flowers remind me that summer sunshine is just around the corner.

When summer arrives, it brings a wonderful abundance of foliage and flowers. This is the main time for hedge trimming, which I consider to be one of the joys of gardening. There are few greater pleasures than standing back and admiring your own work as you sculpt nature into shape.

Autumn is the most romantic of the seasons. The light becomes soft and golden and the garden starts its slow death in a way that is both beautiful and sad. The leaves turn red and gold, one day glowing like beacons in the autumn sun, the next falling to the ground.

There is beauty in a winter garden too, but you have to look carefully to appreciate it. Once the bright autumn colours have faded, you can see other things more clearly, such as the shape and texture of

foliage as well as the great variety of different greens. There are also those magical mornings when twigs and leaves are spangled by a sharp frost.

Gardening Through the Seasons

Read the text carefully and circle the best ending for each sentence.

 Spring appears to be miraculous because
a) the days get longer.
b) of the new growth.
c) summer is not far away.

 The gardener who wrote the piece
a) feels like a sculptor when he cuts his hedges.
b) thinks hedge cutting is the most difficult job for a gardener.
c) thinks hedge cutting is the most important job for a gardener.

 Autumn is the most romantic season because
a) it gets dark earlier.
b) the leaves are red.
c) it is beautiful and sad at the same time.

 In a winter garden it is easier to appreciate
a) frost and snow.
b) bright colours.
c) shapes and textures.

 The gardener who wrote this piece
a) likes one season more than the rest.
b) appreciates each season for different reasons.
c) wishes he could cut hedges all the time.

Express yourself

Have you got a favourite season? Describe the things you like about it.

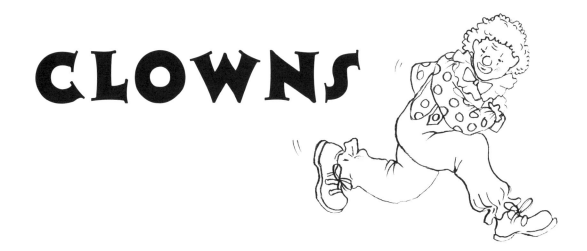

CLOWNS

Toppo comes to school to talk to the kids and sell tickets for the circus in town.

When Jed and Lucy go, Toppo the Clown is very funny in the ring. Afterwards, when they take their little brother to the toilets, they can't believe what they see behind the Big Top. Is that Toppo the Clown running out of the circus manager's trailer? It certainly looks like him, with orange hair and a red nose. What is he carrying? When the children look inside the manager's trailer, what they see sends them running. Who can they tell? Who would believe them?

'*A roller-coaster story, full of mystery and suspense.*'
Gary Marks (*Children's Book Review*)

'*Scary, full of suspense and a good read.*
I'll never think of clowns in the same way again!'
Amanda Donahue (*Children's Book Times*)

'*The perfect read for 8–12-year-olds this summer.*
A gripping story told by the master storyteller.'
Rachel Lemarr (*Kids 'n' Books*)

ISBN 1-85503-363-5

9 781855 033634

£5.95

Clowns

Read the text carefully and circle the best answer to each question.

1. Toppo probably goes to the circus manager's office to
   a) get changed.
   b) ask for more money.
   c) do something bad.

2. The children are not sure it's Toppo because
   a) clowns all look similar.
   b) Toppo is still in the circus ring.
   c) it is very dark.

3. The book is for
   a) toddlers and young children.
   b) pre-teens.
   c) late teens.

4. The comments about the book are by
   a) parents of young children.
   b) circus clowns.
   c) people who write about children's books.

5. In a book shop, you would probably find this book under
   a) comedy.
   b) mystery and suspense.
   c) horror.

Express yourself

Think of a book you have enjoyed reading. Write the description for the back of the paperback. Make it sound interesting and remember not to tell the whole story!

Sporting Talk

'Now, I want you to go out there and show them Stanford are the best! We *are* the best. Got that? We've already shown them that no one can beat us – not on our home field; not away. We've trained for this and we're ready to carry off the championship . . .'

'All right now, quieten down, boys. Save all your energy for out there. Remember, keep your eye on the ball and, Matthew, we're counting on you to make those saves – just like you did last week. Now at half-time I'll talk to you again in here. But right now – let's go out there and show them! Just think of that big silver cup sitting in the school hall. Come on, are we ready? That's the spirit! Now, go out there and *win*!'

Sporting Talk

Read the text carefully and circle the best answer to each question.

 1 This speaker is probably talking to
a) a tennis squad.
b) a football team.
c) a netball team.

 2 The speaker must be
a) a player.
b) the goalie.
c) the coach.

 3 The match is probably
a) in the first round.
b) a friendly.
c) a final.

 4 They must be
a) in a bus.
b) in the changing rooms.
c) on the field.

 5 The players are probably
a) schoolchildren.
b) professionals.
c) adults.

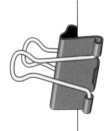

Express yourself

Writing like this, that has the speech of only one person is called a monologue. Write your own monologue for a sports coach, a teacher or some other person who is talking to a group.

Strange Flying Object Alarms Residents

A STRANGE flying object was reported by residents of Kimberly Road, Woodside, last Monday evening. It came out of the sky at about 7 p.m., flying low over Woodside Hospital.

Mr Ray Jones of 4 Kimberly Road said: 'I was just getting the kids ready for bed when I heard a strange noise overhead. I looked out of the bathroom window and couldn't believe what I saw. It looked like a flying dinner plate.' Jane Winters, a neighbour, said: 'It had strange lights coming from it. It was not like a normal aircraft.' The local police said they had received over 100 reported sightings of the object. Professor O'Reilly, an expert on UFOs, commented: 'This could not be a plane because Woodside isn't on any aircraft flight path. More importantly, small pieces of hot burning metal dropped from the sky in the Kimberly Road area . . . and our tests have revealed that it's a type of metal not known on Earth. This seems like a very clear example of a visit from an alien life form.'

Report by Bob Hackman

F.Godfrey 2013 O.Rowe

Strange Flying Object Alarms Residents

Read the text carefully and circle the best answer to each question.

1 The flying object was the shape of a
a) circle.
b) rectangle.
c) triangle.

2 Mr Jones looked out of the window because
a) he was getting his kids ready for bed.
b) he wondered what the noise was.
c) he was in the bathroom.

3 It was unlikely to be a plane because
a) it had lights.
b) it made a strange noise.
c) planes do not normally fly over the area.

4 The professor thinks it's a UFO mainly because
a) he is a UFO expert.
b) 100 people reported it.
c) it dropped pieces of a strange metal.

5 The professor thinks that inside the strange craft there were
a) ghosts.
b) beings from another planet.
c) some people playing a trick.

Ask yourself

Is there life on other planets? Do you think we
are visited by spacecraft from other planets?
Give reasons for your answers.

What Has Happened to Lulu?

What has happened to Lulu, mother?
What has happened to Lu?
There's nothing in her bed but an old rag doll
And by its side a shoe.

Why is her window wide, mother,
The curtain flapping free,
And only a circle on the dusty shelf
Where her money-box used to be?

Why do you turn your head, mother,
And why do the tear-drops fall?
And why do you crumple that note on the fire
And say it's nothing at all?

I woke to voices late last night,
I heard an engine roar.
Why do you tell me the things I heard
Were a dream and nothing more?

I heard somebody cry, mother,
In anger or in pain,
But now I ask you why, mother,
You say it was a gust of rain.

Why do you wander about as though
You don't know what to do?
What has happened to Lulu, mother?
What has happened to Lu?

Charles Causley

E. Berg A. Panayitou
O. Rowe Jan '14

What Has Happened to Lulu?

Read the text carefully and circle the best answer to each question.

 Lulu has disappeared along with
a) her rag doll.
b) her savings.
c) all her shoes.

 Lulu is probably
a) a baby.
b) an old lady.
c) a teenager.

 Mother feels
a) relieved.
b) sad.
c) content.

 The weather is
a) wet and windy
b) hot.
c) wintry.

 The person asking the questions is probably Lulu's
a) father.
b) best friend.
c) brother or sister.

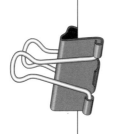

Express yourself.

What do you think has happened to Lulu?
Write the mother's answers to the questions in the poem.

Look carefully at the text and circle the best answer to each question.

Day trip

Andy:

Sam, that you?

Sam: 1

   a) Yes, it is. Who's that?
   b) No, it's not. It's his mother.
   c) Yes, thank you.

Andy:

It's me, Andy. Hey, what
are you doing Saturday?

Sam: 2

   a) I'm busy. I've got tennis coaching all day.
   b) Saturday? Nothing I don't think.
   c) I've been ill in bed all day.

Andy:

Oh, that's good. We're going to the beach
for the day and my dad says you can come
with us. Should be great! Can you come?

Sam: 3

   a) I don't like the beach – it makes me seasick.
   b) Cool! I'll ask Mum when she gets in and call you back.
   c) That's a great idea, you bet I'll come.

Andy:

That's fine. I hope it's OK with her.
Oh, and we're having fish and chips at that
place on the pier before we come home.

Sam:

a) Uggh, not that greasy place!
b) Great idea!
c) I love ice cream.

Andy:

Remember to bring some money.
Call me as soon as you know if
you can come. Bye!

Sam: 5

a) My parents are so strict.
b) See you next week. Bye!
c) Yes, I will. Bye!

Andy:

Bye!

Find out for yourself

Do you use a mobile phone? What do people say
are the advantages and the drawbacks? Can they
be dangerous? How can they be useful?

hacker

Sophie entered her password. Nothing happened. That was strange. She entered it again. She heard clicking noises and tried to stay calm. Just then, words started to type themselves across the screen.

Can't get into your own files? I'm in already. Try again, stupid!

Who was that? She typed her password a third time . . . nothing. Then more words appeared on the screen.

Sorry, but I've changed your password. So you can't get in. What a pity. Meanwhile I can read all your private files. Ha, ha, ha!

A hacker! Someone had got into her files. One of those files had the designs for the Zoomerang! She had to stop them!

Too late, stupid. I'm in and, yes, I can see all your files. Aha, I think I've just found what I've been looking for. Yes, the Zoomerang designs! You really shouldn't have made it so easy for me to get in! It's no fun!

Who was he? Or she? Sophie wanted to ask but she could not even get in to type her questions. 'Stop! Who are you?' she shouted at the screen. No one would be safe if those plans fell into the wrong hands . . . A last message scrolled across the screen.

They already have, my friend. Bye bye.

Hacker

Read the text carefully and circle the best answer to each question.

 1 The screen is
   a) on a television.
   b) on a computer.
   c) at a cinema.

 2 A hacker is someone who
   a) gets into your private computer files.
   b) writes you messages.
   c) helps when your computer breaks down.

 3 Sophie can't open the files on her computer because
   a) her computer is broken down.
   b) she has forgotten the password.
   c) the hacker has changed her password.

 4 The Zoomerang is probably
   a) a secret weapon.
   b) a medicine.
   c) a new board game.

5 The hacker knows what Sophie is thinking because
   a) Sophie writes the hacker messages.
   b) the hacker can read Sophie's thoughts.
   c) the hacker can hear Sophie shouting.

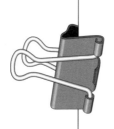

Express yourself
Write a story about technology going wrong.

Room for Improvement

Dad: That's much better. You've really worked hard! It looks much nicer like this, don't you think?

Eric: Yes, but it's so hard to keep it like this, Dad. It all gets messed up so quickly.

Dad: I know it's hard, Eric, but why don't you just put things back as you go along? Then it wouldn't get into such a state . . . and I wouldn't have to nag you.

Eric: I do try, but I'm always in a rush to get to school, or to go and see my friends, or . . .

Dad: I know, I know! Life is one big rush for me too. Look, perhaps you could decide to spend just ten minutes on it every day.

Eric: What, you mean like after school?

Dad: Or before you go to bed.

Eric: But I need more space for all my things – that football, my judo stuff, the frisbees and . . . all my clothes!

Dad: Mmm . . . that's true. Well, there's that old wardrobe in the garage. Why don't we get that up here?

Eric: But it's so . . . so . . .

Dad: Well, sure, but we'll paint it up and it'll look quite different. Come on, let's go and bring it up.

Eric: Oh . . . OK. But, Dad? I get to choose the colours . . .

Dad: Oh, whatever . . . Come on!

Room for Improvement

Read the text carefully and circle the best answer to each question.

 The speakers in the dialogue are talking about
a) a living room.
b) a bedroom.
c) a garage.

 Dad is pleased because Eric
a) worked hard at school.
b) won a judo match.
c) tidied his room.

 Eric does not have enough
a) space for his things.
b) time to see his friends.
c) clothes.

 Dad thinks Eric should try to
a) plan his time better.
b) spend less time with his friends.
c) not rush so much.

 At first Eric doesn't want the wardrobe, probably because it's
a) too big.
b) rather ugly.
c) his mother's.

Ask yourself

Do your parents nag you about anything? Is there something your parents want you to change or do differently? If you were a parent, what do you think would be the best way to get your son or daughter to change their behaviour?

The Big Game

It was the day of the big match. Our home team were sure to win.

'Come on, Hal,' said Dad. 'Let's have our pizza and go. We don't want to miss the game.' Mum had left pizza in the microwave. We ate it and left.

The roads into town were busy. Everyone seemed to be going to the stadium. I sat beside Dad in the front seat, dreaming. One day I'd score the winning goal for my team. The next thing I remember is the sound of brakes. Something was pushing our car off the road. I blacked out.

When I came round, bright lights were shining straight into my eyes and men and women in green gowns were bending over me.

'It's okay, sonny,' said one of the assistants. 'You're doing fine.'

'Where's . . . How's . . . my dad?' I asked, suddenly struck with fear.

'Your dad's doing OK too. In fact he's in better shape than you. You'll be able to see him after your operation. Ah, here's the surgeon coming now . . .'

I couldn't see anything: the light was in my eyes. Then I heard the surgeon coming into the room, coming close; could see the green gown, but no face.

I heard the surgeon gasp. Did I look that bad?

'I . . . I can't treat this child. It won't be allowed.'

'Whatever's the matter?' asked the assistant.

'This patient . . . is my son.'

Conran Jan 2014
Freddie
39

The Big Game

Read the text carefully and circle the best answer to each question.

 1. Hal is going to watch a
a) baseball game.
b) football match.
c) tennis tournament.

 2. The car must have
a) got a flat tyre.
b) been hit by another car.
c) hit a wall.

 3. Hal wakes up
a) in hospital.
b) in the home team's changing rooms.
c) in the car.

 4. Hal is worried that his dad
a) went to see the game without him.
b) would miss the game.
c) was badly injured.

 5. The surgeon must be Hal's
a) father.
b) stepfather.
c) mother.

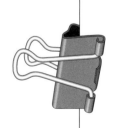

Ask yourself

Are there any jobs that are still done mainly by men and any still done mainly by women? Do you think men or women are better at certain jobs? If so, which ones? Why?

TREASURE HUNT

Towards the end of the summer holiday I decided to go out and dig for treasure. It sounds stupid, but when you're *really* bored, anything sounds like a good idea. Finn seemed up for it, so we started at the huge old oak tree in our garden.

Finn is a better digger than me. He's smaller, but just seemed to know what he was doing. Our pile of earth grew. Then my shovel hit something hard. Before long, I heaved it out of the ground. Finn wanted to, but since the whole thing had been my idea, it was only fair.

I was sure the gigantic bone had belonged to a dinosaur and that we should take it to the museum immediately. I laid it down on the grass to see if there was anything else in the hole. When I turned back, both Finn and the bone were gone.

Finn didn't come back until late. I was furious he had returned without the bone. Mum thinks he'd buried it again. I think he spent the afternoon chewing on it. I've dug for treasure a few times since, but I never take Finn.

Treasure Hunt

Read the text carefully and circle the best answer to each question.

 1 The person telling the story is
a) an old person.
b) a child.
c) an animal.

 2 The person telling the story
a) is told what to do by Finn.
b) tells Finn what to do.
c) does not like Finn.

 3 The person telling the story
a) thinks the bone may be a fossil.
b) wants to eat the bone.
c) is greedy.

 4 The person telling the story
a) didn't trust Finn.
b) lied to Finn.
c) didn't realise what Finn would do.

 5 Finn is
a) a dinosaur.
b) a thief.
c) a dog.

Express yourself
Rewrite the passage, but from Finn's point of view. Imagine how the episode must have looked to him.

THE DEATH OF PHAETON

In Greek mythology, Apollo the Sun god pulled his chariot across the sky every day to give light to the Earth. Apollo's son was a proud young man called Phaeton. He did not live on Mount Olympus with the other gods, but on Earth.

One day, Phaeton climbed to the top of Mount Olympus. Apollo was overjoyed to see him and took him to see his greatest joy.

'These are my horses. They pull the Sun chariot across the sky each day. They are wild, strong creatures.'

Phaeton begged his father to let him drive the chariot. Apollo said no, but Phaeton would not stop begging. Eventually Apollo gave in.

'Hold the reins tightly or the horses will run away. Follow the tracks in the sky and do not turn from the path.'

The horses galloped off and Apollo watched in horror as they pulled the reins from Phaeton's grip. The Sun chariot shot up to the heavens and set fire to the stars. Then, plunging down towards Earth, it dried up the lakes and boiled the seas.

Zeus, the powerful ruler of the gods, saw the horses running wild. He saw the Earth and its people burning. He had to act. He struck Phaeton with a bolt of lightning, turning him into a shooting star. The fiery star plunged into the ocean and disappeared.

Conran 2013

The Death of Phaeton

Fill in the gaps, choosing the best word or phrase from the text.

⟨1⟩ Every day, Apollo the Sun god gave light to the Earth by

driving _____ .

⟨2⟩ In Greek mythology, the gods lived on

_____ .

⟨3⟩ Apollo described his horses as _____ .

⟨4⟩ When the Sun chariot went up to the heavens,

it _____ .

⟨5⟩ Phaeton was turned into a shooting star when Zeus struck him

with _____ .

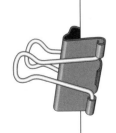

Find out for yourself
Find out some of the names of other Greek gods
and what jobs they did.

The Redwoods

The tallest trees in the world are found on the west coast of North America. They are called redwoods. A fully grown redwood is so tall you can't see its top and so wide that even if you had six adults holding hands they couldn't reach around the trunk.

Redwoods need a long time to grow to their great heights. The long hot summers and warm rainy winters of the Pacific coast provide ideal growing conditions. The daily fog brings water to the trees, even if there is no rain.

There are other reasons why these trees live long and healthy lives. Redwoods have very thick bark, so that insects and other pests, which could damage the inside of the trees, can't get in. Fire is a great danger to trees in hot climates, but the redwoods are well protected. Their thick bark only burns at extremely high temperatures, so it is almost fireproof. Also, the parts of the tree that burn most easily – the branches and needles – are so high up that fire almost never reaches them. Finally, because the huge branches of the redwoods prevent sunlight

reaching the forest floor, not many smaller plants grow beneath them. This means fires do not start there easily.

These amazing trees can keep living and growing for 2,000 years!

Trees

The Redwoods

Fill in the gaps, choosing the best word or phrase from the text.

1 Redwood trees are found on _____.

2 These trees grow best when they have _____

   and _____.

3 Even if there is no rain, the trees get water from

   _____.

4 The branches and needles of the tree rarely burn because they

   _____.

5 You won't find many _____ under a

   redwood because the branches make it so shady.

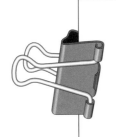

Express yourself

Write a story imagining that you are an ancient, wise redwood tree. Describe some of the things you have seen in the forest over the centuries.

A Matter of Taste

Imagine how dull it would be if you could only taste four flavours. Do you know what? You *can* only taste four. The rest is done by smell!

Your tongue is covered by tiny bumps called taste buds. There are four different types. The ones on the tip of your tongue taste sweet things; the ones at the back taste bitter things and the other two types lie on the sides of the tongue and taste salty and sour things.

So when you think you are tasting chocolate ice cream, you are really smelling it. It's hard to believe, but think about when you have a bad cold. You may have noticed that food doesn't taste as good, even though it's not your tongue that is poorly. This is because when you eat, minute particles from the food rise into the air and you breathe them in. The particles land on the tiny hairs inside your nose. The hairs send signals to the brain and you smell the food. When you are eating, you think of the smell as the taste. If your nose is blocked and the particles cannot get to the hairs in your nose, you are left with the four flavours that your tongue can taste.

The Body

A Matter of Taste

Fill in the gaps, choosing the best word or phrase from the text.

① _____ are tiny bumps that cover your

tongue.

② The taste buds at the _____ of your

tongue taste bitter things.

③ You can't taste things as well when you

_____.

④ When you eat, you breathe in _____.

⑤ You can taste only the four flavours detected by your tongue

when _____.

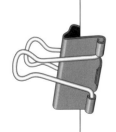

Express yourself

Imagine your favourite taste. Now try to describe it. This won't be easy; you will have to think hard for some good adjectives!

Hailstorms

Hailstorms can be frightening. At their worst, they can break windows, flatten plants and even kill small animals. Hailstones are balls of ice that can grow to be as big as golf balls. But strangely, it can hail in the summer. So where does the ice come from?

Every hailstone starts out as a raindrop. When a raindrop passes through a cold layer of air in the atmosphere, it freezes to become a tiny ball of ice. Before it reaches the ground, wind carries it back up into the warmer air again. There, more raindrops stick to the little ball of ice. As it falls back through the cool air, the water sticking to the ball freezes too, making the hailstone bigger. If it is still light enough, a hailstone may bounce back and forth between the cold and warm air several times, and it gets bigger each time.

Eventually, the hailstone will fall to the ground. Some are large enough to do serious damage and would hurt you if you were unlucky enough to be hit. Hailstorms can be very exciting to watch, as long as you are safe inside!

Hailstorms

Fill in the gaps, choosing the best word or phrase from the text.

1 Hailstones are made of _____.

2 A raindrop is turned into a ball of ice when it moves through

_____.

3 The hailstone is carried back into the warmer air by

_____.

4 Each time the hailstone moves back and forth between the warm

and the cool air, it _____.

5 If you are indoors, watching a hailstorm can be

_____.

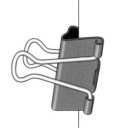

Find out for yourself

Find out about some of the most extreme hailstorms there have been and what damage they have done.

Tour de France

Every year in France, a group of cyclists starts a 2,500 mile race through the French countryside. Nearly 100 competitors start the race, but only one can win. It is called the 'Tour de France' and it takes every ounce of determination and staying power that the cyclists possess – just to finish.

Each day of the race represents one stage. A stage can be as long as 140 miles and may take the cyclists up and down the most gruelling French mountain roads. At the end of each stage, the cyclist in the lead is given the coveted yellow jersey to wear for the next stage.

When legs are wobbly and bodies are tired and hungry, the temptation to give up or to simply stop and rest is huge, but in the Tour de France every moment counts. Cyclists eat, drink and even go to the toilet while remaining on their bikes. Some injured cyclists receive medical treatment as they cycle along, not wanting to waste one precious second.

The winner of this race receives glory and fame as well as the yellow jersey. But anyone who just completes this agonising feat has won a personal victory they will never forget.

Tour de France

Fill in the gaps, choosing the best word or phrase from the text.

① In the Tour de France, cyclists race over

_____ miles.

② A _____ is worn by the cyclist in the lead.

③ Cyclists who are tired and hungry often feel tempted to

_____ or to _____.

④ _____ can be given to injured cyclists

whilst they are still on their bikes.

⑤ There is only one winner of the race, but everyone who finishes has

achieved _____.

Express yourself

Have you ever attempted anything that was very difficult and succeeded? Write about what happened. What were your thoughts before you started and while you were doing it?

Getting to Know Your New Video

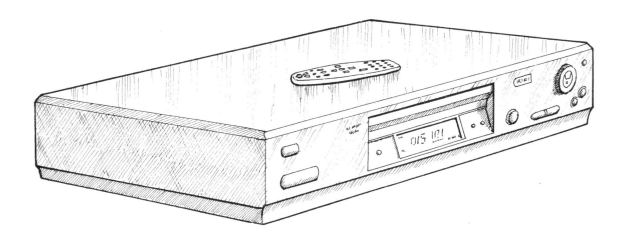

Initial installation

1 Open up the battery compartment of your remote control and place the batteries inside.

2 Close the battery compartment.

3 Confirm the picture on the TV screen by pressing the OK button on the remote control.

4 Connect the aerial to the video recorder, then press the OK button. Auto install will then start and this picture will appear on your screen:

> AUTO INSTALL
>
> YOUR VIDEO RECORDER IS NOW
> SEARCHING FOR ALL AVAILABLE CHANNELS
>
> 02 CHANNELS FOUND
>
> PLEASE WAIT

Wait until all TV channels have been found. This can take several minutes.

5 When Auto install is complete, 'AUTO INSTALL COMPLETE' will appear on the screen.

6 To end, press the MENU button.

The initial installation is now complete.

Getting to Know Your New Video

Fill in the gaps, choosing the best word or phrase from the text.

1 To confirm the picture on the TV screen, use the remote control and

press _____.

2 Before you press the OK button again, the aerial should be plugged

in to _____.

3 It could take _____ to find all the TV

channels.

4 After Auto install is complete, you should

_____.

5 When you have followed these steps you should have completed

_____.

Express yourself

Do you prefer to watch a film at the cinema or at
home on a video? Explain your answer.

FOOD

Tea-drinking Going to Pot

Putting on the kettle for a 'cuppa' is in decline. The number of cups of tea drunk in the home has fallen by 13 per cent in the past 5 years, and coffee by 6 per cent. Nowadays people are turning to the fridge for soft drinks, fruit juice and mineral water.

Bill Gorman of the Tea Council said, 'Tea has never been cool with kids and now we have a couple of generations who have grown up without drinking tea.' He blames the 'Coca-Cola and Pepsi boys' for hot drinks becoming less popular. He also believes that now that more women go to work, there are fewer coffee mornings or invitations to tea with their friends and their children.

Just 30 years ago, 50 per cent of all fluid drunk in Britain was tea; today it is down to 40 per cent. The move away from hot drinks is mirrored by a fall in the sales of jam, marmalade and honey. It's possible the two trends could be linked, since fewer people are sitting down to a traditional family breakfast.

Tea-drinking Going to Pot

Fill in the gaps, choosing the best word or phrase from the text.

1. Tea-drinking in the home has fallen by _____

   in the past 5 years.

2. Instead of drinking tea and coffee, people are choosing

   _____ .

3. _____ do not think that it is cool to

   drink tea.

4. Tea accounts for _____ of all drinks

   consumed in Britain today.

5. As well as drinking less tea, people are also buying less

   _____ .

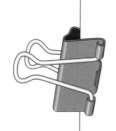

Ask yourself

Do you think it is good or bad that people are drinking less tea and coffee? Give reasons for your answer.

Fill in each gap, choosing the best word or words from the list of possible answers.

The Story of Arachne

There once lived a woman who was the finest
①_____ in the whole world. Her name
was Arachne. She soon became famous for her
exquisite designs. She also became proud and boastful.

'Not even the goddess Minerva, who weaves cloth
for the gods, can weave as well as me.'

Minerva heard about the ②_____
young woman who claimed to be better than her.
Furious, she came to search the Earth until she
found Arachne.

'So you think you are a better weaver than me?'
said Minerva to the ③_____ Arachne.
'We shall both weave a length of cloth and see whose is more glorious.'

Without speaking, Arachne set up two looms and they went to work. Minerva's
cloth was all the colours of the rainbow. It sparkled and shimmered as one colour
blended into the next. But Arachne's cloth dazzled the eyes; it looked as if it was
made of gold and studded with ④_____ .

Minerva knew she was beaten. In her jealous rage, she sprinkled magic water on
Arachne. Immediately, the woman began to shrivel and shrink. Within minutes, she
was a tiny brown spider. Never to ⑤_____ again, Arachne spent her
life weaving webs.

①	a) builder	b) weaver	c) cook	d) spider
②	a) lovely	b) ugly	c) proud	d) clever
③	a) surprised	b) relieved	c) sleepy	d) angry
④	a) nails	b) studs	c) eggs	d) jewels
⑤	a) weave	b) boast	c) shrink	d) sing

Express yourself

Tell the story of Arachne from her point of view.

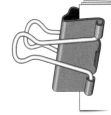

Fill in each gap, choosing the best word or words from the list of possible answers.

Do Fish Have Ears?

Have you ever noticed that fishermen are usually quiet? If they were too ①_____ the fish would hear them and swim away. But how can fish hear? They haven't got any ②_____!

Actually, fish do have ears, but they are inside their heads, just behind the eyes. Fish ears work quite differently from those of other animals. All fish have a bag, called the 'air bladder', in their bodies. The air bladder receives any ③_____ and sends the vibration to a part of the fish's ear that is like a box. The box is full of little stones called 'otoliths'. The otoliths vibrate and the fish 'hears' the sound.

The fish's ears also help it to stay the right way up in the water. Each fish ear has three hollow bones, ④_____ like horseshoes. The bones are filled with liquid which moves when the fish moves, giving it a sense of ⑤_____. If something went wrong with these bones, the fish would swim on its side, or even upside down.

① a) busy   b) noisy   c) clumsy   d) funny

② a) ears   b) fins   c) brains   d) money

③ a) music   b) gifts   c) bumps   d) sounds

④ a) polished   b) strong   c) shaped   d) coloured

⑤ a) style   b) balance   c) humour   d) direction

Find out for yourself

Try and find out how the human ear works. Find a diagram of the ear and make your own drawing of it.

Fill in each gap, choosing the best word or words from the list of possible answers.

Shooting Stars

On a clear summer's night, it is wonderful to see a shooting star, streaking across the dark sky and 1_____ towards the Earth. But did you know that they are not stars at all? They are pieces of rock and metal. In fact, the correct name for a shooting star is a meteor.

There are millions of 2_____ in space, but we cannot see them until they get close to the Earth. When a meteor approaches the Earth, it passes through the atmosphere, starts to glow and eventually burns. The burning meteor is what we see from 3_____ and call a shooting star.

Often, meteors travel through space in 4_____ that are called 'swarms'. Each swarm has an orbit, just like a planet, and each year it will pass close to the Earth at a point in its orbit. One well-known swarm has been named the 'Perseid' swarm and it can be seen every August.

Most meteors are small and burn up completely before they reach the ground. Some meteors, however, are very large and crash into the Earth. Most hit so 5_____ that they are buried deep in the ground. Once a meteor has landed on the Earth, we call it a meteorite. One enormous meteorite that landed in Africa weighed 70 tonnes!

1   a) wandering   b) strolling   c) zooming   d) hopping

2   a) meteors   b) aliens   c) stars   d) planets

3   a) the atmosphere b) the Earth   c) Britain   d) the Sun

4   a) rockets   b) disguises   c) gangs   d) groups

5   a) loudly   b) fast   c) slowly   d) silently

Express yourself
Write a poem about a meteor racing through space and then falling to Earth. Describe its speed and the way it starts to glow and burn as it comes close. You could make it sound beautiful, or perhaps menacing and scary.

Fill in each gap, choosing the best word or words from the list of possible answers.

The Appian Way

Rome

Today, we are used to the roadways changing as new roads are being built and old ones improved. In Italy, there is a road called the Appian Way that is over ①_____ years old and is still used today.

It was built by the Romans when they were expanding their empire. Their armies needed to be able to ②_____ up and down the country, so in 312 BC the Roman emperor ordered a road to be built. It was to stretch from Rome to the southern end of the country we now call Italy. The emperor at that time was called Appius Claudius and the road was named ③_____ him.

Appius took a great interest in the construction of the road, and even though he was blind, he used to ④_____ the road with his feet to make sure that it was smooth enough.

It took 16 years to build and by the time it was finished, Appius Claudius had died.

Modern road builders are amazed at how well the Appian Way was constructed. In places, the road is 1.5 metres thick. Today, roads are only half that thickness, even though they have to carry much ⑤_____ loads. It was clear that the Romans built their roads to last – and they have!

①	a) 2	b) 200	c) 2,000	d) 20,000
②	a) drive	b) dance	c) march	d) fight
③	a) after	b) before	c) above	d) below
④	a) tickle	b) feel	c) stamp on	d) scratch
⑤	a) wider	b) stronger	c) more important	d) heavier

Find out for yourself

There were many Roman roads built in Britain.
Find out where some of them ran to and from and
what they were called.

Fill in each gap, choosing the best word or words from the list of possible answers.

Origami

Have you ever practised the ①_____ of origami? If you have ever made a paper aeroplane, then you have.

Paper was ②_____ 2,000 years ago by the Chinese and the ancient art of origami dates back to that time. When a person died, the Chinese used to make little paper houses with furniture inside. The paper models stood for all the things waiting for their loved one in the next world. As time went on, people folded paper for less ③_____ reasons; they did it simply to make beautiful things.

Around the year 600, the Chinese introduced paper folding to Japan. The Japanese quickly became the greatest origami artists in the world. The tradition is still strong there today.

Some paper figures, such as fishes, lobsters and cranes, were thought to bring good ④_____. People decorated their houses with all sorts of designs, including elaborate flowers and peacocks.

Origami made its way to Europe approximately 500 years ago when Japanese magicians ⑤_____ to Italy. It became quite a craze, with even kings and queens and famous artists such as Leonardo da Vinci learning how to fold paper.

①	a) recipe	b) art	c) lesson	d) practice
②	a) invented	b) eaten	c) ripped	d) worshipped
③	a) happy	b) terrible	c) Chinese	d) serious
④	a) tradition	b) food	c) fish	d) luck
⑤	a) wrote	b) flew	c) travelled	d) swam

Express yourself

Find a book about origami and make your own origami model.

Fill in each gap, choosing the best word or words from the list of possible answers.

Think Before You Speak

'I'm bored, bored, bored,' moaned Alice to her mum. 'I'm so ①_____ , I could bang my head against the wall.'

'What about ②_____ your bookshelves like you promised?' suggested her mum, who was trying to do her work at the kitchen table.

'I don't feel like it.'

'Well, call a friend and invite them round.'

'I have. No one's in. They're probably out, having fun.'

Alice's mum put down her pen, closed her books and held out her ③_____ .

'Come on, then.'

'Where to?'

Alice's mum led her into the garden, where the afternoon sun was the hottest it had been all year.

'Close your eyes and don't move. I'm going to cure your ④_____ .'

Alice closed her eyes and wondered what her mother was going to do. Alice didn't guess that she was tiptoeing over to the garden tap. As quickly as she could, Alice's mother turned on the tap and aimed the hose at her unsuspecting ⑤_____ . Almost before she had opened her eyes, Alice was drenched.

'Now,' said her mum with a smile, 'you go and get dried and changed while I finish my work. If you get bored again, don't hesitate to come and tell me, will you, darling?'

① a) happy   b) excited   c) bored   d) intelligent

② a) tidying   b) building   c) destroying   d) talking to

③ a) foot   b) hand   c) pen   d) tongue

④ a) illness   b) headache   c) boredom   d) hay fever

⑤ a) daughter   b) son   c) Alice   d) face

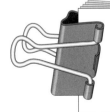

Express yourself

Write a story in which something very unexpected happens that makes you forget your boredom.

Fill in each gap, choosing the best word or words from the list of possible answers.

Matilda

ROALD DAHL is surely one of the most well-loved children's writers. His books are popular all over the world and have been translated into French, Russian, Arabic and Chinese. In fact, you can read Roald Dahl in 34 different ⟨1⟩_____.

The film versions of Roald Dahl's stories, such as *Charlie and the Chocolate Factory* and *The Witches*, are very entertaining. *Matilda* is another of his books that was made into a film. This is the tale of a young girl with special ⟨2⟩_____. Matilda can calculate any sum in her head and make things move with her mind. Her parents and older brother don't know this and are horrible to poor Matilda. Her father tells her not to read so much and wants her to watch more TV!

At school, Matilda and all the children are ⟨3⟩_____ of Miss Trunchbull, the cruel, ugly principal. Miss Trunchbull likes to shut children in her nasty dark cupboard.

Only Matilda's teacher, Miss Honey, understands that the girl has special powers. In the end, Matilda uses ⟨4⟩_____ to drive Miss Trunchbull away from the school and she is adopted by her teacher. Miss Honey becomes the new principal and everyone is happy, ⟨5⟩_____ Matilda.

⟨1⟩	a) books	b) countries	c) languages	d) nations
⟨2⟩	a) ideas	b) powers	c) eyes	d) maths
⟨3⟩	a) terrified	b) proud	c) jealous	d) thinking
⟨4⟩	a) that	b) it	c) him	d) these
⟨5⟩	a) apart from	b) thanks to	c) instead of	d) during

Express yourself

Write a review of a film you have seen. If possible, choose a film based on a book you have read. Which did you enjoy more? Why?

Fill in each gap, choosing the best word or words from the list of possible answers.

Walt Disney World

Disney

WALT DISNEY loved dreaming up stories to tell and new ways to tell them. After he died, his brother, Roy, kept one of his biggest ①_____ alive. He made sure Walt's special 'world' was built just the way Walt had imagined it. Roy even insisted that it be called *Walt* Disney World, so ②_____ would know it was his brother's dream.

Walt Disney World ③_____ opened on 1 October 1971. Since then, millions of people have come to visit. Some come for a day, but most stay a little longer. There's so much to see and do. The most ④_____ part of Walt Disney World is the Magic Kingdom. It's home to Cinderella Castle, Space Mountain and those rascally Pirates of the Caribbean. It's also where Mickey, Minnie and their ⑤_____ have their country cottages. Kids of all ages can't get enough of this happy place.

① a) nightmares   b) pot plants   c) dreams   d) brothers

② a) no one   b) everyone   c) their mother   d) Americans

③ a) officially   b) briefly   c) nearly   d) definitely

④ a) boring   b) famous   c) dangerous   d) secret

⑤ a) characters   b) parents   c) enemies   d) friends

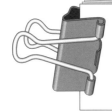

Find out for yourself

Find out 5 things you didn't already know about Walt Disney.

Answers

Getting the main idea

William Shakespeare
1) a. 2) a. 3) c. 4) b. 5) c.

Wolf Children
1) a. 2) c. 3) c. 4) b. 5) a.

Working Dogs
1) a. 2) b. 3) c. 4) a. 5) c.

Diana, Princess of Wales
1) b. 2) a. 3) c. 4) a. 5) b.

Bettacare Mail Order
Catalogue
1) c. 2) b. 3) b. 4) a. 5) c.

Spinning
1) a. 2) b. 3) c. 4) a. 5) b.

Super Soups
1) b. 2) a. 3) c. 4) b. 5) a.

Brekkypops
1) c. 2) a. 3) c. 4) c. 5) c.

Gardening Through the
Seasons
1) b. 2) a. 3) c. 4) c. 5) b.

Making inferences

Clowns
1) c. 2) a. 3) b. 4) c. 5) b.

Sporting Talk
1) b. 2) c. 3) c. 4) b. 5) a.

Strange Flying Object Alarms
Residents
1) a. 2) b. 3) c. 4) c. 5) b.

What Has Happened to Lulu?
1) b. 2) c. 3) b. 4) a. 5) c.

Day Trip
1) a. 2) b. 3) b. 4) b. 5) c.

Hacker
1) b. 2) a. 3) c. 4) a. 5) b.

Room for Improvement
1) b. 2) c. 3) a. 4) a. 5) b.

The Big Game
1) b. 2) b. 3) a. 4) c. 5) c.

Treasure Hunt
1) b. 2) b. 3) a. 4) c. 5) c.

Noting details

The Death of Phaeton
1) his chariot across the sky
2) Mount Olympus
3) wild, strong creatures
4) set fire to the stars
5) a bolt of lightning.

The Redwoods
1) on the west coast of
North America
2) long hot summers,
warm rainy winters
3) the daily fog
4) are so high up
5) smaller plants

A Matter of Taste
1) taste buds
2) back
3) have a bad cold
4) minute particles from
the food
5) your nose is blocked

Hailstones
1) ice
2) a cold layer of air
3) wind
4) gets bigger
5) very exciting

Tour de France
1) 2,500
2) yellow jersey
3) give up, stop and rest
4) Medical treatment
5) a personal victory

Getting to Know Your New
Video
1) the OK button
2) the video recorder
3) several minutes
4) press the MENU button
5) the initial installation

Tea-drinking Going to Pot
1) 13 per cent
2) soft drinks, fruit juice and
mineral water
3) Kids
4) 40 per cent
5) jam, marmalade and honey

Using context clues

The Story of Arachne
1) b. 2) c. 3) a. 4) d. 5) b.

Do Fish Have Ears?
1) b. 2) a. 3) d. 4) c. 5) b.

Shooting Stars
1) c. 2) a. 3) b. 4) d. 5) b.

The Appian Way
1) c. 2) c. 3) a. 4) b. 5) d.

Origami
1) b. 2) a. 3) d. 4) d. 5) c.

Think Before You Speak
1) c. 2) a. 3) b. 4) c. 5) a.

Matilda
1) c. 2) b. 3) a. 4) d. 5) b.

Walt Disney World
1) c. 2) b. 3) a. 4) b. 5) d.